Here Come
The Cottontails!

BY ALICE E. GOUDEY

Illustrated by Garry MacKenzie

Charles Scribner's Sons
New York

We are grateful to Lee S. Crandall, General Curator Emeritus
of the New York Zoological Society, for reading and
checking the text of this book.

Here Come The Cottontails!

The first light of morning is beginning to creep over the quiet meadow where Mother Cottontail crouches in her resting place under a small juniper bush.

Her ears lie flat along the back of her neck. She twitches her nose as she smells the pine odor of the juniper. Now and then she dozes for a few seconds, never quite asleep.

Suddenly the spring breeze that sweeps across the meadow brings a new smell to her. Instantly she is alert, her ears raised high, listening. Every muscle in her soft, furry little body quivers with fear.

She turns her ears first in one direction and then in another. But she hears nothing.

The breeze carries the scent to her again, stronger than ever.

The scent means danger. It comes from the fox whose den is in the hillside across the valley. He has almost caught Mother Cottontail several times. Then she feared only for herself. But now she fears for her four babies.

They were born just last night. They are so tiny and so helpless. She has hidden them in a nest under a wild rosebush not far from her own resting place.

What if the fox finds them?

She knows what she must do if this happens. But first she will wait. There is no need for her to dash out from under the juniper bush until she knows where he is. She "freezes," not a muscle moves.

Without turning her head she peers out through the overhanging boughs. Her bulging eyes make it easy for her to see in all directions.

Now she sees the fox coming through the meadow. He springs into the air several times as if enjoying himself. No doubt he has aroused some sleepy grasshoppers and is catching them.

Then he pounces on something. It is probably a meadow mouse. She watches while he stops to eat it.

If he comes too close to her helpless babies she must leap from her hiding place and lead him away from their nest even though it may mean death for herself.

She watches with pounding heart while he passes the juniper bush and the wild rose-bush.

Then he turns and starts back, nose to the ground, sniffing.

With a bound, Mother Cottontail springs from beneath the bush and dashes across the meadow with the fox close behind her.

She does not run in a straight line. She dodges and swerves and zigzags, making it hard for the fox to follow her.

But in spite of all her tricks she can hear him close behind her. Because she cannot outrun the fox, her only chance is to get to some hiding place where she will be safe.

Mother Cottontail has lived in the meadow for almost a year and has come to know every inch of it. She knows every clump of grass, every bush and all of the good safe places.

Now she leads the fox toward an old brush pile that lies near the edge of the woods.

As she bounds along, several crows feeding in the meadow rise up ahead of her. She swerves to one side. The crows fly above the fox, cawing and flapping their wings. He pauses to snap at them and Mother Cottontail scurries ahead at full speed.

But the fox is gaining on her when she finally dashes under the brush pile.

She does not stop until she reaches the center of the pile where she crouches, with her heart throbbing against her ribs.

She hears the fox sniffing around outside. She hears the dry twigs crackle as he climbs up on the pile of brush and paws at the top.

At length the noise stops. But fear keeps Mother Cottontail inside. She will wait until the fox is far away and she has stopped quivering. It is safe and cool here and she has little to worry about now.

She has been in the brush pile many times before. At those times she nipped off twigs with her sharp strong teeth, making a network of little pathways through the brush.

While she rests, a meadow mouse patters along one of the paths. The meadow mouse has nothing to fear. Mother Cottontail is one of the gentlest creatures that lives in the meadow. Although she has sharp teeth she seldom uses them against any other living thing unless she or her babies are in danger.

When she is rested she creeps cautiously from under the brush pile, stopping to twitch her nose and turn her ears for the scent and sound of danger.

All seems safe. She hops toward her resting place, or form, under the juniper bush, never getting far from a bush or clump of grass that she can hide under.

But what about her little ones? Have they been harmed while she has been away?

She circles the wild rosebush where her babies sleep, not going too near. She must not go too close to them during the daylight hours lest she lead an enemy to their nest.

Pausing, she raises herself slightly on her hind legs in order to see better.

At last, satisfied that everything is all right, she settles down in her form to doze for the rest of the day.

When darkness comes she goes to nurse her babies. As she draws near to them, she gives a long leap that carries her under the bush. She must not leave any tell-tale tracks or scent around the nest.

Before her little ones were born she pulled hair from her breast and mixed it with leaves and grass to line the nest and make a blanket.

Now she carefully pulls aside the blanket and nuzzles each baby gently with her nose. Then she crouches above them so they can nurse. They drink her milk eagerly for they have not eaten since the night before.

Each cottontail is about four inches long and weighs little more than an ounce.

When they were born their bodies were pink and hairless. But now, just a day later, they are covered with short, soft fuzz.

Their ears lie flat on their heads, and only tiny lines show where their eyelids will open in about six days.

When they finish nursing, Mother Cottontail looks down at her little ones as they squirm and push against one another.

How soft they are!

And how tiny!

Before she leaves she covers them again with the blanket of matted leaves and fur, and then scatters a few leaves and grass above it.

Soon the little cottontails are asleep, their small stomachs bulging with warm milk.

The meadow is bright with moonlight when Mother Cottontail leaves the nest.

She circles about, stopping to nibble the spring grasses and the tender green shoots.

She sees a skunk digging for grubs in the lower end of the meadow. It is best to stay away from him.

A deer steps out of the woods to browse on the shrubs and grass. He is nothing to be afraid of.

But when she hears the hoot of an owl she scurries back to her form under the juniper bush.

In the days that follow, Mother Cottontail is never far from the nest of her little ones.

One day she hears a rustling sound. She knows what the sound means even before she sees the bull snake crawling through the grass toward the nest.

A bull snake could easily swallow every one of her babies!

She is out of her form in one quick bound. She must do what she can to save them. She will rake the snake with the strong claws on her hind feet. She will bite it with her sharp teeth.

There is no dodging or swerving now as she races straight for the snake.

But a shadow moving swiftly over the ground makes her crouch low and squeak in terror. Looking up, she sees a red-tailed hawk swooping down upon her.

She scurries toward the nearest bush. If only she can reach it and crawl in among its heavy stems near the ground perhaps she will be safe.

As she scuttles under the bush the hawk
crashes down on top of it.

The hawk flaps his wings to balance himself on the small branches that bend under his weight.

Then he ruffles his feathers and looks around. He is angry. Where has his prey disappeared to so suddenly?

In a moment his eyes catch the movement of the bull snake in the grass. A snake is better than nothing.

He pounces on it at once and flies away with the snake dangling from his claws.

Every night, as soon as it is dark, Mother Cottontail goes to the nest to feed her babies. Even though she feeds them only at night they grow rapidly.

In about a week their eyes are wide open and their ears stand up straight. Their small bodies are covered with coats of soft, fluffy gray-brown fur.

Now they are becoming so restless, so full of life, so eager to be out of the nest and hopping about that Mother Cottontail is more watchful than ever.

One night, when she goes to feed them, four little heads pop up and eight bright eyes look out before she reaches the wild rosebush. She thumps her hind leg on the ground to warn them. Down go the little heads at once.

Young cottontails must be careful. They must stay hidden until they are strong enough to run and escape their enemies.

But before she reaches the nest they peek out again.

One evening, when they are twelve days old, the first little cottontail leaves the nest. Five tiny hops take her beyond the sheltering branches of the bush.

The second follows, then the third, then the fourth little cottontail is out in the big strange world.

Mother Cottontail does not thump on the ground; it is useless to try to keep her restless children hidden any longer.

But on their first night out in the strange new world the little cottontails are shy and timid. They stay close beside their mother. They twitch their tiny noses to catch the night smells and move their ears to catch the night sounds.

The hooting of an owl down in the woods and the barking of the fox on the hillside make them quiver and crouch low to the ground.

But it is not long before the first cotton-tail to leave the nest is nibbling the tender grass around her. Little Nibbler's brothers, too, try the grass and find it juicy and good.

Long before daylight they are back in their nest again, four furry little bunches snuggled close together, sound asleep.

Little Nibbler and her brothers grow stronger with each passing day. Each hop grows longer and they venture farther and farther from their mother and their nest.

At night they romp and play in the bright moonlight, for night is the best time for little cottontails.

Countless other bright-eyed creatures that love the night come out from burrows in the ground, from crevices in the rocks and from holes in hollow trees.

Bats flit through the darkness catching insects. Moles and shrews, meadow mice and dainty white-footed mice scurry through the grass. And flying squirrels sail from tree to tree like small acrobats.

These furry creatures that love the night do not harm the little cottontails.

Nibbler and her brothers chase one another, jump into the air and play leapfrog
while their mother watches quietly.

But the night also brings out prowlers—the weasels, the skunks and the raccoons. With their keen sense of smell and their eyes that can see well in the dark they search out the little scurriers in the meadow.

Danger can come from above too. The little cottontails learn this one night when a great horned owl swoops down on silent wings and carries away one of Nibbler's brothers.

When Nibbler and her two remaining brothers are about two weeks old they no longer go back to the nest where they were born. Each now chooses a form, or resting place, of his own, near Mother Cottontail.

Nibbler chooses a place in a tall clump of

grass that grows beside a stone. She slips in between the grass stems and sits with her back against the stone so she can look out through the curtain of grass that shields her. Soon the place where she sits is flattened to fit her small body.

The forms of Nibbler's brothers are not far from her own.

During the day the cottontails sometimes go short distances from their hiding places, always alert, always ready to dash for cover. But they spend many hours sitting quietly in their forms, dozing and waiting for dusk to come to the meadow.

It is in the third week of their lives that the worst danger of all comes to them.

First, there is the frightening odor. Mother Cottontail raises herself on her hind legs, looking, sniffing, testing the air for the sound and smell of danger.

Then she sees them—a pair of weasels! They are playing in the middle of the meadow, jumping up in the air and turning somersaults.

There is no time to be lost. Weasels are the worst enemies of all.

The cottontails scurry to their hiding places.

The terrified cottontails crouch in their forms. They are still, still. Only their whiskers quiver as they wait.

The weasels have come from an underground burrow in the pasture beyond the woods. In the burrow their six babies sleep in a nest made of rabbit fur.

When the weasel babies waken, they will be hungry. It seems they are always crying for something to eat. It keeps their parents busy hunting for food to fill their stomachs.

Mother Cottontail sees the two weasels stop playing. Now they start hunting, noses to the ground, darting here and there.

They are small—smaller than she is. But in spite of their size how fierce they are! And how swift! One quick dash and they can fasten their teeth in a furry throat.

There is nothing Mother Cottontail can do. If she runs they will be upon her in an instant. Even if she could hide in a stone pile or in a brush heap they would slip in after her.

She sees them scuttle past her form. Then she sees them dash forward. She hears two sharp squeaks.

A few seconds later she sees the weasels lope off across the meadow, each holding a little cottontail in its mouth.

After the dreadful night of the weasels

only Little Nibbler and her mother are left.

They spend the next two weeks together, eating grass and sedge and chickweed, circling the meadow, stopping to eat wild strawberry leaves and the glossy leaves on the wild blueberry bushes.

At the end of the two weeks Nibbler is restless, and wanders farther and farther away from her mother.

Mother Cottontail does not pay much attention to Nibbler. Sometimes she is even cross. She has found a mate and is going to have another litter of babies before long. She must start to make a new nest.

It is time for Nibbler to find a meadow of her own and take care of herself.

One evening she starts out to find a new home.

The underside of her short fluffy tail gleams white as cotton as she makes her way toward the upper part of the meadow.

A thicket of low bushes grows at the

upper end of the meadow. Here Nibbler stops to eat a few blackberry leaves and then crosses over a ditch.

After scrambling up a bank beyond the ditch she finds herself in a place where there are no bushes or grass to hide in. This is quite frightening. Nibbler has never been on a road before. It stretches out ahead of her, long and bare.

Suddenly there is a dreadful noise. Bright lights blind her. She does not know which way to turn; she scurries first in one direction and then in another.

At last she crouches down in the middle of the road, unable to move, as two great lights come toward her.

The car passes over Nibbler with a terrifying swoosh, leaving her fur rumpled and full of dust. But at least the heavy wheels did not run over her small body.

Frightened almost out of her wits, she scurries into the nearest field and hides under a clump of grass. Here she rests during the night.

At dawn Nibbler is on her way again. Shortly after sunrise she comes to a meadow that seems much like her old home meadow.

She circles about, exploring. Yes, there are plenty of green plants to eat here — plenty of grass and sedge. There is a pile of stones in the corner, and a little farther on, a tangle of brush to hide in.

Not far away is a small spruce tree with overhanging boughs. A few hops and a long jump and she is under them. This is a fine place for her first form in her new home.

But before Nibbler settles down to rest she must clean her coat.

She rakes and combs her fur with the claws on her hind feet, twisting and turning to reach her back, her haunches and her undersides.

She scrubs her face with her forepaw. Then, stretching out her hind legs, one at a time, she cleans and licks them.

Stickers and burrs are tangled in her fur. These she nips out with her teeth.

When she has made her fur soft and fluffy

and clean again she settles down in her form to rest and doze.

The summer months that follow pass peacefully for the little cottontail. Food is plentiful. She visits a farmer's garden and in a single night eats half a row of beans that have just come through the ground. She feeds on his lettuce too.

But the barking and baying of a beagle tied up in his yard sends shivers through her. And one night she barely escapes the claws of the farmer's big tom cat. After that she does not go back to the garden.

By October Nibbler is almost fully grown. She is fat, her fur is glossy and she weighs about two pounds.

By the end of October the autumn wind shakes the last leaves from the trees. The grass is no longer green and juicy; it is dry and brown and does not taste good. A cotton-tail must hunt other food.

Nibbler now visits the thickets, and eats the bark from the canes of the blackberry and raspberry bushes. She strips the bark from a young black cherry tree as far up as she can reach and nips off the ends of tender twigs wherever she can find them.

One night in December a fierce cold wind howls around the little spruce tree, twisting and bending it.

But by morning the wind has stopped blowing and all is quiet.

Nibbler pokes her head through the spruce boughs and looks out on a smooth white world.

She sniffs the cold, crisp air and steps out cautiously. She takes one hop and sinks into the soft fluffy snow up to her ears. Turning quickly, she goes back under the spruce tree.

She stays in her form all day and does not go out again even at dusk.

That night, rain falls, freezing and making a hard icy crust on top of the snow.

Before morning the rain stops and a light sprinkling of snow comes down and covers the icy crust.

At dawn Nibbler ventures out again. This time she does not sink down; the icy crust beneath the sprinkling of snow supports her slight weight.

With each hop her hind feet land in front of her forefeet, making two tracks, one slightly behind the other.

As she crosses the meadow she leaves behind her a trail of little footprints in the snow.

As the cold winter days go by, Nibbler stays huddled in her form under the little spruce tree much of the time. Now and then she goes out to chew bark from the trees or to eat small twigs.

When she is not dozing she peers out from between the spruce boughs and watches her neighbors in the meadow.

She sees the little meadow mice scamper across the snow, leaving dainty tracks behind them. She watches as they climb the tough grass stems to eat the tiny seeds that cling to the tops. Some of the seeds fall on the snow, and the sparrows flutter down to pick them up.

At last winter is over. The snow melts, leaving the ground dark and moist.

Nibbler wiggles her nose. What a good smell! There is the promise of young green shoots and tender grass in the air.

That evening she hears the shrill call of the spring peepers, the little inch-long, gray-green frogs that live down in the pond. Their bell-like voices say that spring has come to the meadow.

Within a few weeks a soft carpet of green grass covers the ground, and leaves unfold on the bushes and trees.

One evening she sees another cottontail in the meadow. He has never been there before.

Who is he?

She raises herself on her hind legs in order to see better. He looks very much like herself. He is grayish-brown with large ears and a small fluffy tail that is as white as cotton on the underside.

The cottontail hops toward Nibbler as she waits.

When he is within a few feet of her she bounds away, and he follows close behind her.

But Nibbler is not afraid. This is different from being chased by a weasel or a dog.

She jumps high in the air and the cottontail, unable to stop so suddenly, dashes under her. Then she turns and bounds away in a different direction.

The cottontail follows and is always close behind her as she jumps into the air again and again. He has come to the meadow to be Nibbler's mate.

But within a few days Nibbler no longer enjoys running and playing with her mate. She is cross, and nips him. She turns on him and pulls a big bunch of fur from his hind leg and chases him away.

Three weeks later she chooses a place to make a nest in a clump of grass not far from her form. She is going to have her first family of babies in about a week and must have a nest ready for them.

With her forepaws she digs until she has made a little shallow bowl-shaped place in the earth about three inches deep. She lines it with leaves and grass. Then she pulls fur from her breast and puts it in the nest to make it warm and soft.

But that night a little meadow mouse finds the nest. Stuffing as much fur in her mouth as she can she patters off with it. She returns again and again until she has carried away the last bit.

Fur makes a nice lining for her nest too.

The following morning Nibbler discovers the robbery. She is tense with fear. There is no doubt that some animal has found her nest. Now she must make another one. It would not be safe to put her babies in this one.

She chooses a new nesting place under a low-spreading juniper bush. Its overhanging boughs make a fine sheltering roof.

Nibbler works steadily until the new nest is finished.

In about a week it will cradle her babies.

Then, in the night, she will go quietly and cautiously to feed them just as her own mother went to her little ones.

The Black-Tailed Jack Rabbits

Mother Jack Rabbit stretches out a long, lean hind leg and scratches her ear with the claws on her foot. Then she crouches low in the shade of a mesquite bush, her long ears flattened.

Beyond the shade of the mesquite bush the Arizona desert lies hot and dry under the afternoon sun.

There are few animals about. Most of them have disappeared into their underground burrows or are resting in a spot of shade to escape the desert heat.

Mother Jack Rabbit glances toward the bur sage bush where her little ones are hidden. Everything seems all right. The desert is quiet. Nothing is stirring except a horned lizard that scoots across the sand and hides under a cactus bush.

She closes her eyes for a few seconds. When she opens them again she sees a road runner dashing madly back and forth like a fussy old hen that has lost her wits.

The freakish looking bird is a rascal. There is no doubt about it. It has bold bright eyes, a wicked looking beak and long legs. It walks with a quick, springy step as it plunges headlong first in one direction and then in another.

The road runner has a long tail, and coarse blue-black feathers that stick straight up on the top of its head.

Mother Jack Rabbit does not take her eyes from the road runner for an instant. If it comes too close to the nest under the bur sage bush she must be ready to dash out and draw its attention to herself.

The wicked bird could pick up one of her babies and slam it down on the ground, or against a stone, and break every bone in its tiny body.

Then her eyes catch a movement in the little clumps of grass that dot the desert. A rattlesnake is crawling from one spot of shade to another.

If it chooses the shade under the sage bush that surely will be the last of her little ones. The rattlesnake could swallow them alive.

Then Mother Jack Rabbit sees the road runner pause, tail feathers erect. Suddenly it darts toward the snake, first from one direction and then from the other, always staying out of reach of the terrible fangs.

The road runner darts about so fast that the snake does not have time to coil so it can spring and strike.

But at last, worn out with twisting and turning, the rattlesnake gives up and tries to streak off through the grass.

But before it has gone far the road runner pounces.

The bird, seizing the snake at the back of the head, shakes it and slams it on the ground again and again.

Finally the rattlesnake lies limp and still.

Then, with a powerful thrust of its beak, the road runner pierces the skull of the rattler and eats its brain.

Having finished its meal, the bird plunges off through the mesquite and sage bushes, clicking its beak.

Still alert and quivering, Mother Jack Rabbit listens. But there is no sound now except the soft humming of the desert breeze as it blows through the hundreds of prickly spines that grow on the cholla trees and the giant cactus trees.

She settles down again and closes her eyes. She will stay under the mesquite bush until the hot sun goes down and evening coolness comes to the desert.

Mother Jack Rabbit's buff-gray coat with its sprinkling of darker hairs blends in with the soft colors of the desert sands. She is so nearly the same color as her surroundings that it is hard to see her when she is not in motion.

She is not a soft little creature like Mother Cottontail. She is lank and lean and wiry. She is about twenty-five inches long while Mother Cottontail is only about fifteen inches long.

Mother Jack Rabbit has long seven-inch ears tipped with black, and a short black tail that is white on the underside.

Her hind legs are long and strong and can send her bounding across the desert.

But, like Mother Cottontail, she goes quietly and cautiously at night to feed her little ones.

Now, as the purple dusk settles over the desert, she leaves the mesquite bush and goes to the nest in the bur sage bush where her babies are snuggled in their fur-lined nursery.

The little jack rabbits are only a day old. They were born with fur covering their small bodies. Unlike many newborn animal babies', their eyes were wide open. Within a few minutes after they were born they could take a few steps. From the very first moment of their lives they were not as helpless as the little cottontails.

Before the baby jack rabbits have finished nursing, dusk changes to darkness. Large bright stars come out and sparkle in the blue-black sky. The clearness of the desert air makes them seem close to earth.

The night is cool, and now the desert comes alive with hordes of little creatures that have hidden away from the daytime heat.

Mother Jack Rabbit hears them rustling and scurrying over the sand as they romp and play and feed and scuffle.

When her little ones have finished nursing she covers them with fur and grass, and with a long bound, leaves the nest.

As she nibbles here and there on scattered clumps of desert grass she watches the little night creatures around her.

She sees a trade rat pattering along on its tiny white feet, carrying a twig in its mouth. But when it sees a shiny pebble it drops the twig and picks up the pebble.

The trade rat is forever "trading" something it has for something different. There is no telling what it will finally take back to its cluttered nest.

A little kangaroo rat hops about on its hind legs, holding its stubby forepaws against its chest. Its long fur-tipped tail trails behind.

The little kangaroo rat is sometimes called The Mouse That Never Drinks. This is because it does not need to drink water to stay alive. It can manufacture water in its own body.

Mother Jack Rabbit watches the tiny creature. She sees it stop and fill its cheek pouches with seeds that grow on the tips of desert grass. And not far away a little elf owl looks out into the night from its hole in a giant cactus tree.

Before the night is over Mother Jack Rabbit nibbles on the prickly pear cactus. She chews around a patch of the sharp pointed spines that grow on the leathery cactus "leaves" and carefully pulls it out. Then she pokes her nose into the opening and eats the juicy pulp she finds inside. She must be very careful or the sharp spines may stick in her flesh.

But she needs the juicy pulp to keep her alive. Although Mother Jack Rabbit can go for a long time without drinking water she cannot manufacture it in her body as the little kangaroo rat does. She must eat juicy, or succulent, plants that give her moisture.

It is daylight when she finishes eating the prickly pear cactus, and the little night creatures are scurrying back to their burrows.

She hears a gilded flicker call from its perch on a giant cactus. She sees a cactus wren fly from its nest among the bristling spines of the cholla tree. Then a warning smell comes to her.

She knows at once it is the smell of her enemy, the coyote. Twisting and turning her ears, she hears him brush against a bush quite near her. She crouches low and flattens her long ears.

When the coyote is almost upon her she suddenly springs up like a small explosion.

The startled coyote jumps back, and before he has time to start running, Mother Jack Rabbit is off and away with a good head start.

Her long hind legs send her bounding over the desert, fifteen feet to a jump.

She looks back but cannot see the coyote, so she springs up four feet above the ground. Then she sees him racing toward her.

The coyote is the only enemy in the desert that can run as fast as a jack rabbit. At full speed each can run forty-five miles an hour.

Mother Jack Rabbit flattens her ears, digs her toes into the sand and runs low to the ground. Then she uses one of her tricks; she dodges in and out among the scattered bushes.

Another "spy" hop into the air tells her she has left the coyote farther behind. He has not been able to follow her dodges.

She slows down now and scuttles under a

creosote bush. The twisted branches and the glossy green leaves of the bush hide her. Here she is safe.

When she is rested she goes back to her form under the mesquite bush, and that night she goes again to feed her babies.

Within a few days she can no longer keep her little ones in the nest. One morning when she returns from a night of feeding she finds them nibbling on the tips of desert grass.

In about four weeks the little jack rabbits leave the nest and each finds a resting place beneath a bush. Now they find their own food and take care of themselves.

They have probably learned some things by watching their mother. But, like all wild animals, they were born knowing how to take care of themselves. This "knowing" without being taught is called instinct.

The little jack rabbits do not fear the lizards that scoot across the desert floor. Nor do they fear the round-tailed ground squirrels and the many different kinds of rats and mice. But they run for cover when they see the shadow of a horned owl or a red-tailed hawk. And they come to know the danger of a coyote, a road runner and the many different kinds of rattlesnakes.

If the jack rabbits can escape their enemies, they may live for ten or twelve years and raise many little ones of their own that will go bounding across the Arizona desert.

Hares, Cottontails and Rabbits

Almost everyone uses the word "rabbit" when speaking about the small rabbit-like animals that live here in North America. But if we were to speak correctly we would call them hares and cottontails.

Hares have long, strong hind legs. Their ears too are long, sometimes measuring as much as eight inches. Compared with other members of the rabbit family hares are quite large, sometimes weighing seven and a half pounds. There is one exception. That is the little Pika which will be described later.

Hare babies are well developed when they are born. Their eyes are open, their bodies are covered with fur and they can hop about a few minutes after birth.

The animal we commonly call a "jack rabbit" is really a hare.

There are several different kinds of jack rabbits in North America beside the Black-tailed which you have read about in the earlier part of this book. Among them are the White-tailed jack rabbit, the White-sided jack rabbit and the Antelope jack rabbit.

We find jack rabbits living not only in our deserts but also on our open western plains.

We have other hares in North America in addition to the jack rabbits. One of them is the Varying Hare, sometimes called the Snowshoe Rabbit.

It has large feet that are covered with thick, long fur in winter. On these "snowshoes" it can hop about in deep, soft snow or travel on slippery ice without skidding.

In summer the Varying Hare is a brownish color but in winter it wears a coat of snowy white.

It is found in Canada and in the northeastern part of the United States. It is also found in some of our western mountains.

The largest hare in North America is the Arctic Hare that lives in the snow around the North Pole.

During the short northern summer its coat is a grayish-brown. But during the long winter the Arctic Hare is as white as the snow itself except for black tips on its ears. Even the sharp eyes of the wolf, the fox and the snowy owl have a hard time seeing it as it crouches in the snow.

The smallest hare is the little Pika that is only about six inches long. It is a fine-haired, silky little creature that wears a coat so nearly the same color as the rocks it lives among that it is very hard to see unless it is in motion.

The Chippewa Indians called the Pika Little Chief Hare because it sits hunched up among the rocks like a tiny Indian chief. The Chippewas used its fine silky fur to make clothing for their babies.

The Pika is also called Little Haymaker, because it nips off grass and thistles and stems of plants and spreads them out to dry in the warm summer sun. When its "hay" is dry, the little Pika stores it under overhanging ledges of rock to use for food when winter comes.

Pikas live in colonies among the rocks in our high barren western mountains.

They also live in Alaska, China, Mongolia and India.

Cottontails are smaller than hares. They weigh only two or three pounds. Their ears too are shorter, being only two to three inches long. Their hind legs are short compared with those of the hares.

Cottontail babies are born with their eyes closed, and their tiny pink-skinned bodies do not have any fur on them. Unlike the frisky baby hares the little cottontails are completely helpless at birth.

There are five groups of North American cottontails – the Mountain Cottontail, the Eastern Cottontail, the Desert Cottontail, the Brush Cottontail and the New England Cottontail.

Some variety of cottontail may be found

in all of our states. They are also found in Mexico and in the northern part of South America. All varieties like to live in places where there are bushes and brush in which to hide.

Now let us consider the "real" or "true" rabbits. The name "rabbit" was first given to a family of small animals native to northern Africa and southern Europe. Later they were introduced into other European countries and into England.

When the first settlers came to America they called the small rabbit-like animals they found here "rabbits," and most of us continue to do so even though it is not exactly correct.

The scientists say that the European and English rabbits are the "true" rabbits. These rabbits are very much like our cottontail except they are burrowers, living in underground burrows or warrens.

No doubt Peter Rabbit who disobeyed his mother and went into Mr. McGregor's garden was a "true" rabbit as the story about him came to us from England.

Hares, cottontails and rabbits are both harmful and useful to man.

Because they have so many babies each year, it is hard to find enough food for all of them. And so they eat the farmer's crops and gardens and chew the bark off young trees as far up as they can reach. They also eat the canes of raspberry and blackberry bushes.

Too many jack rabbits can nibble a pasture bare. It has been estimated that fifteen antelope jack rabbits can eat as much food as one sheep.

When the western plains are dry and the grass turns brown the jack rabbits have been known to travel in hordes to farms that are irrigated. Here they find fresh green food. They can eat the farmer's entire crop in one night.

Hares and cottontails sometimes have a contagious disease known as tularemia. In order to protect ourselves it is best not to handle one of the little animals if it appears to be sick.

Since the discovery of our country we have found hares and cottontails to be useful if not about in too great numbers.

They furnished the early settlers with meat during the winter when food was scarce. The soft furry skins were used for warm robes and for clothing.

Even today many people who live in the country depend on them for a part of their meat supply. "Rabbit" meat is sold in many markets in the cities. The skins are used today for fur collars and fur coats. Most of the felt used in hats is made from the fur.

But there is another way in which these small animals are very important to us. They are important because they give us so much pleasure. Even though they may annoy us when they eat our food it would certainly be a great loss never to be able to see a shy little cottontail along the roadside or in the meadow, or a long, lean jack rabbit bounding across the western plains.

DATE D

FORM 393 SCHOOL SPECIALTY SUPP

10/20/6	12-1-84
10/29/69	4-6-88
4/12/7	2-1-90
22-23	12-13-01
23-73	5-12-93
23	
4	
	—